This book belongs to:

....

First published by Pugalugs Ltd in 2014

Written by Jessica Parish
Designed and illustrated by Helen Poole
Edited by Book Helpline

A CIP catalogue record for this book is available from the British Library.

ISBN 978-0-9930479-0-9

Printed and manufactured in China.

Pugalugs Ltd
The Enterprise Centre
Salisbury Street
St Helens
WA10 1FY
www.pugalugs.co.uk

Pugalugs™

The Beginning

Written by
Jessica Parish

To Billy,
I hope you enjoy
the story!
love Jessica

Illustrated by
Helen Poole

This is a story about a little pug puppy called Pugalugs.

Pugalugs was born on the fifth of November, which is easy to remember because it is Bonfire night.

Little puppies are always born with their eyes closed. He was still only two weeks old and he could not see a thing!

Pugalugs was born at the same time as his brother, Dug, and his sister, Bella.

Pugalugs and Bella are both fawn in colour. Dug has a shiny black coat, with a little tuft of white fur on his chest. Bella is much smaller than her brothers.

Pugalugs and his brother and sister belong to a family: Mum, Dad, Granddad and little Connor, and of course, Mummy Pug and Daddy Pug!

They live in a house near a beautiful lake. As the puppies were born in the wintertime the lake was completely frozen, but inside their house, it was nice and warm.

Pugalugs shared a bed with his brother and sister. There wasn't much room in the bed at all! It was a very tight squeeze but at least they were cosy and warm.

The puppies were so squashed together in their bed that sometimes, while they were asleep, they would kick each other in the head with their little paws!

Pugalugs was so small that he was able to fit in little Connor's hand.

He had a curly tail, a scrunched up, flat nose and big floppy ears!

Pugalugs was about to open his eyes for the very first time. He opened his eyes and blinked three times. He looked around at his cosy bed, his brother and sister and his surroundings.

"Wow!" said Pugalugs; he could see everything!

Pugalugs looked around at all of the exciting things that he could see, but then, all of a sudden... "Ouch!" he shouted.

He had been *donked* on the head by a tiny paw!

His brother, Dug, had been stretching out in his sleep and had accidentally kicked him.

Pug puppies love to sleep, and stretch too!

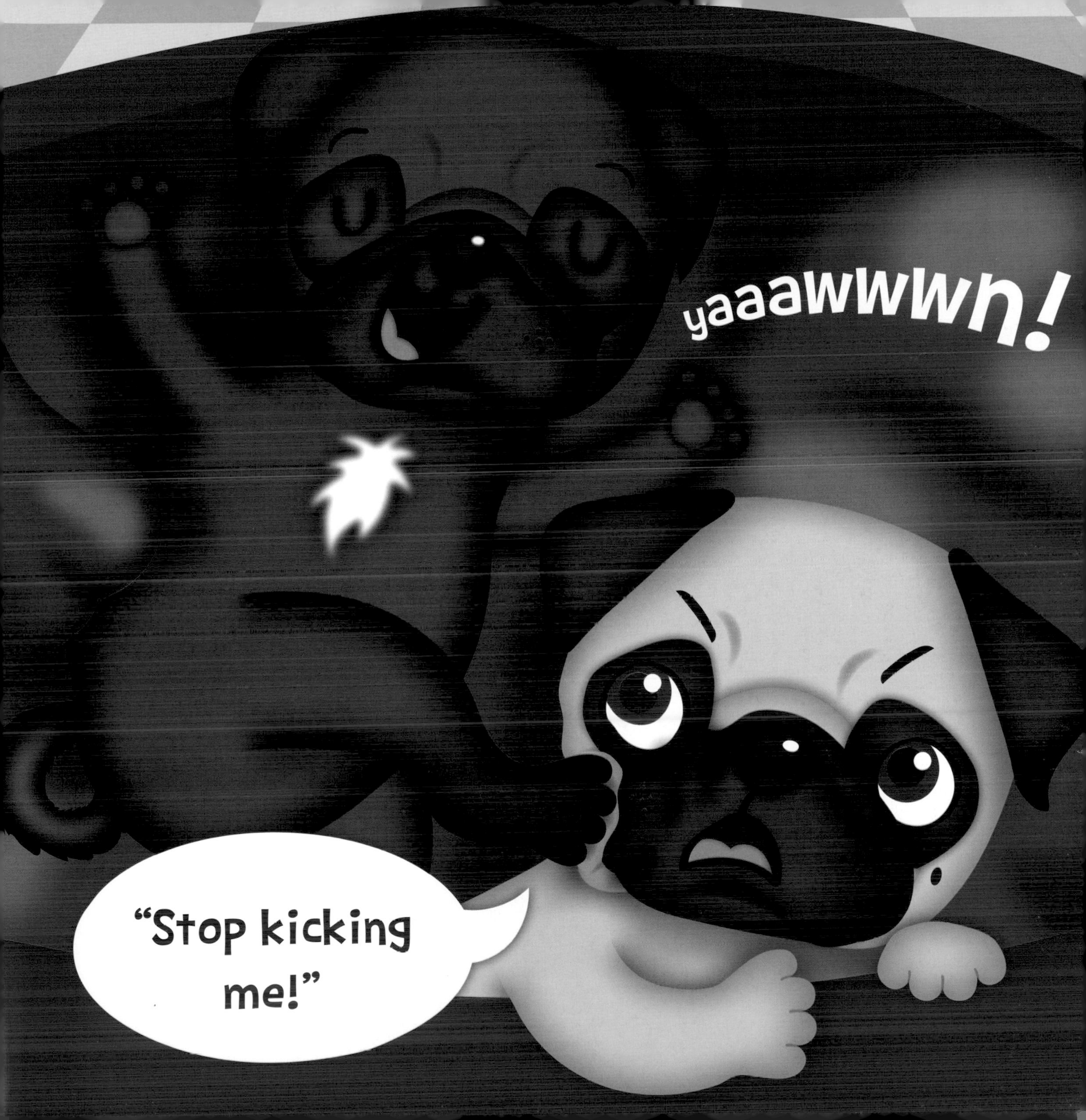
yaaawwwn!
"Stop kicking me!"

Pugalugs was now four weeks old and was growing stronger every day. He decided that it was finally time to climb out of bed and stretch his little legs.

He gathered all of his strength, stood up for the first time and wobbled his way out of bed.
There was no stopping him... once he'd got used to the shiny, slippery kitchen floor!

"Yippee!" said Pugalugs, "here goes!"
It was time to explore this exciting new world.

He stumbled upon a strange object. It was soft and squashy; what could it be? It must be Granddad's slipper!

Puppies love to chew, and they will chew anything they can get their paws on!

Pugalugs was a very lucky puppy. He and his brother and sister had lots of toys to play with.

They were not allowed to play outside yet because they were too young, and it was far too cold for little puppy paws.

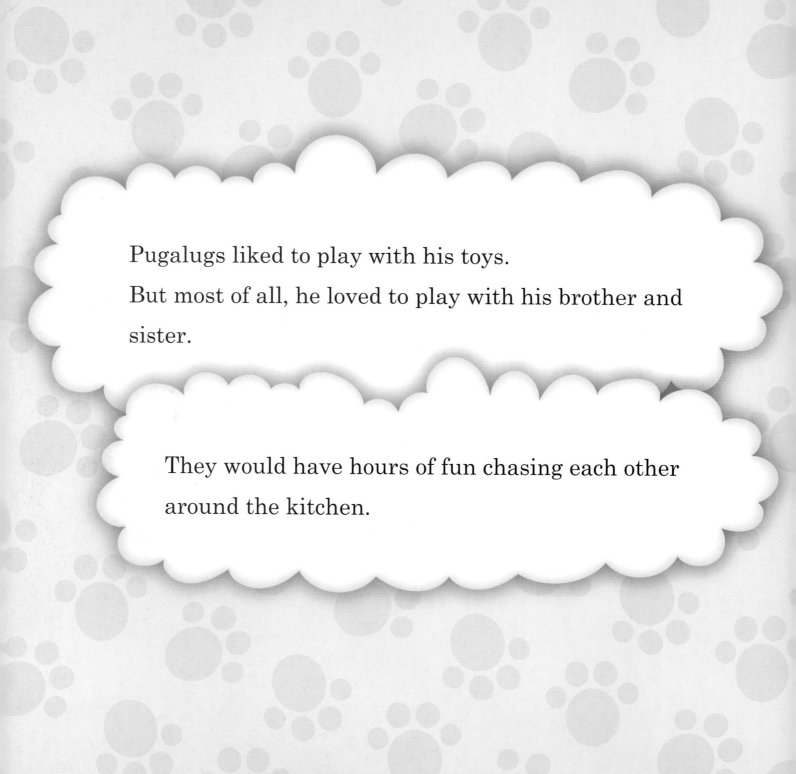

Pugalugs liked to play with his toys.

But most of all, he loved to play with his brother and sister.

They would have hours of fun chasing each other around the kitchen.

Pugalugs was now eight weeks old and loved to eat puppy food. His favourite flavour was chicken. He also *loved* milk!

Pug puppies are hungry all of the time and they are very messy eaters. They get food all over their faces and sometimes their ears too!

Pugalugs liked to eat six times a day. After all, he was a growing pup... and he was growing fast!

After dinner time, Pugalugs liked to take a nap with his brother and sister. They would cuddle up together in bed and make lots of funny noises as they slept.

I bet you didn't know that puppies could snore? Pug puppies do, Pugalugs does!

But Dug was the loudest snorer in the whole house!

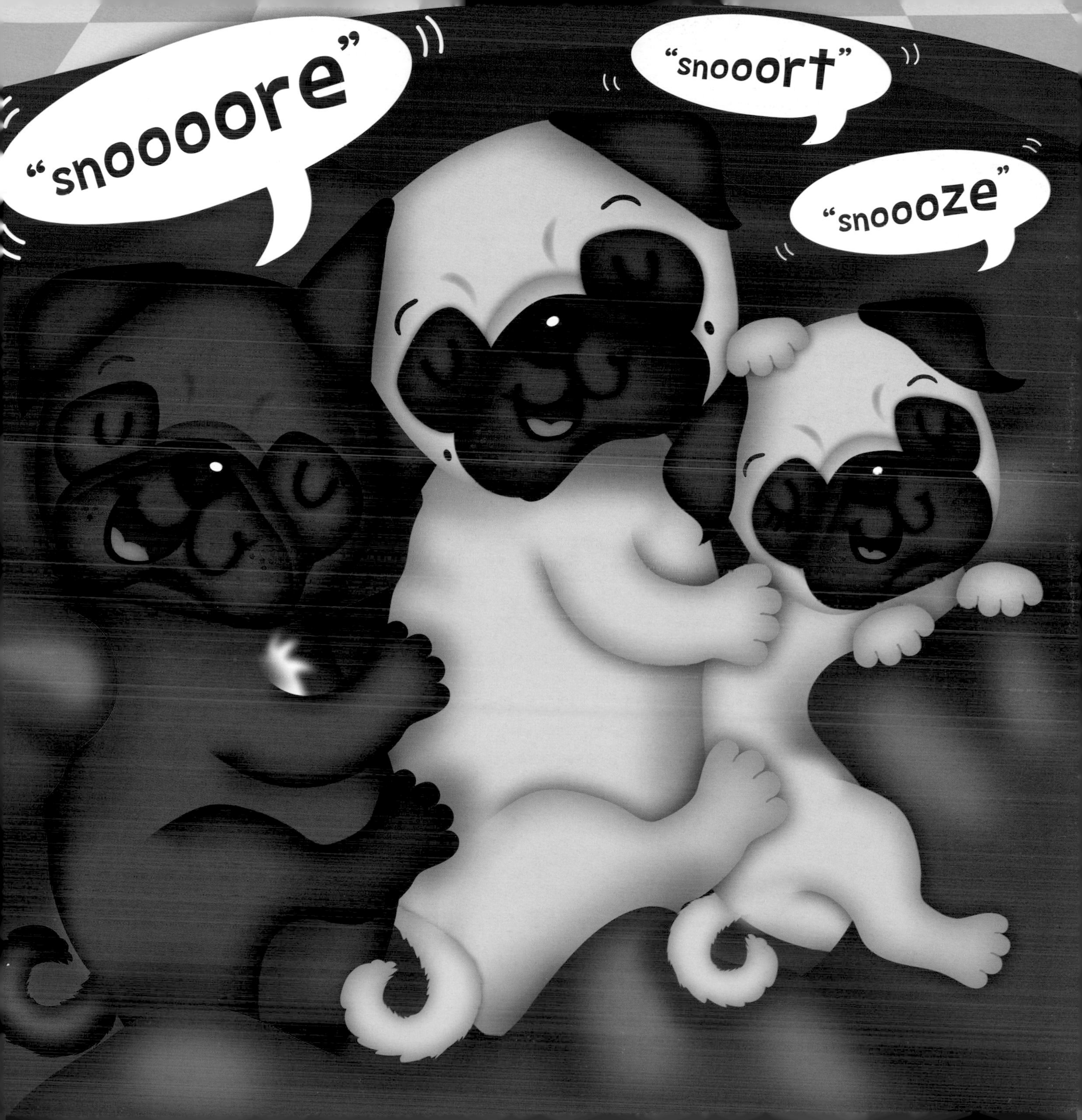
"snoooore"
"snooort"
"snoooze"

After a relaxing puppy snooze, the three pups were full of beans. PLAYTIME!

"Let's go and explore!" said an excited Pugalugs.

Off they went around the house to see what they could find.

"I wonder what's up there?" asked Pugalugs, as he looked up at the tall staircase.

To the puppies, the staircase looked as big as Mount Everest!

They could hardly reach the first step.

Pugalugs was a very curious, little puppy.

He had discovered lots of exciting things inside his home, but what he really wanted to do was play outside.

Unfortunately, he was still only eight weeks old and he would have to wait until he was a little bit bigger and a bit older.

If only he knew what exciting adventures lay ahead...?

To be continued...

Pugalugs

Dug

Bella

COMING SOON!

Look out for the next
Pugalugs book!

The Adventures of Pugalugs: Walkies!

Join Pugalugs on his very first walk!

Who will he meet on this
exciting adventure?

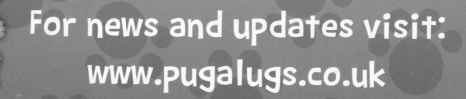

For news and updates visit:
www.pugalugs.co.uk